How do I use th[...]

Key Words with Peter an[...] parallel series, each containing [...] books. All three series are written using the same carefully controlled vocabulary. Readers will get the most out of **Key Words** with Peter and Jane when they follow the books in the pattern 1a, 1b, 1c; 2a, 2b, 2c and so on.

• Series a
gradually introduces and repeats new words.

• Series b
provides further practice of these same words, but in a different context and with different illustrations.

• Series c
uses familiar words to teach **phonics** in a methodical way, enabling children to read increasingly difficult words. It also provides a link to writing.

Published by Ladybird Books Ltd
A Penguin Company
Penguin Books Ltd., 80 Strand, London WC2R 0RL, UK
Penguin Books Australia Ltd, 707 Collins Street, Melbourne, Victoria 3008, Australia
Penguin Group (NZ) 67 Apollo Drive, Rosedale, North Shore 0632, New Zealand

ISBN: 978-1-40930-144-8

Printed in China

Key Words

with Peter and Jane

1c   Read and write

written by W. Murray
illustrated by J.H. Wingfield

After reading Books 1a and 1b the learner should copy out and complete the following pages in an exercise book. Answers are given on Pages 46 to 51 for corrections, revision and testing.

Here is Peter.

I like P____.

The answer is on Page 46

Here is Jane.

I like J_ _ _.

The answer is on Page 46

Here is a dog.

I like the d__.

The answer is on Page 46

Here is a shop.

I like the s_ _ _.

The answer is on Page 46

Here is a ball.

I like the b___.

The answer is on Page 47

Here is a tree.

I like the t _ _ _.

The answer is on Page 47

Here is a toy.
I like the t_ _.

The answer is on Page 47

The s _ _ _ is here.

The t _ _ _ is here.

The answers are on Page 47

The d_ _ is here.

The b_ _ _ is here.

1 Peter and Jane like t＿＿ d＿＿.

2 The dog likes t＿＿ b＿＿＿.

The answers are on Page 48

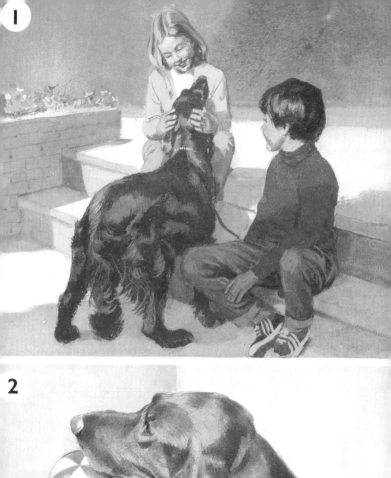

Yes   No

Is Peter here? ___.

Is Jane here? ___.

Is the dog here? __.

The answers are on Page 48

Yes   No

Is Peter in the shop? __.

Is Jane in the shop? ___.

Is the dog in the shop? __.

The answers are on Page 48

Yes   No

Has Jane a
toy? _ _ _ .

Has Peter a
toy? _ _ _ .

Has the dog a
ball? _ _ .

The answers are on Page 49

Peter writes.

Peter likes to write.

I like t_ w____.

The answer is on Page 49

Jane writes.

Jane likes to write.

I like t_ w_ _ _ _.

The answer is on Page 49

1 Peter is in the s___.

The dog is
i_ the shop.

2 The ball is
i_ the tree.

Jane is i_ the tree.

The answers are on Page 50

1 I like t____.

2 I like t___.

3 I like P____ and
J___.

4 I like d___.

The answers are on Page 50

1 trees

2 toys

3 Peter and Jane

4 dogs

1 Jane has t__ d__.

2 Peter has _ b___.

3 The dog h__ a ball.

4 The shop h__ toys.

The answers are on Page 50

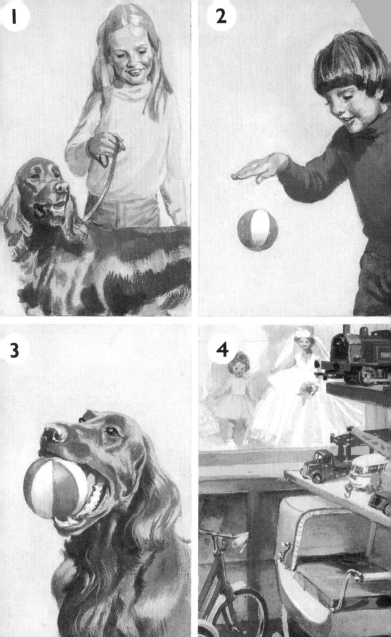

Write out correctly—

1 Jane here is.

2 is here Peter.

3 dog I the like.

4 Peter Jane and dog like the.

The answers are on Page 51
The use of flash cards may be helpful with these exercises.

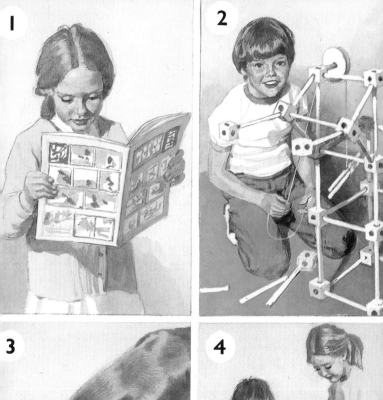

Write out correctly—

1 Here toy a is .

2 tree Here is a .

3 like toys I .

4 tree a in toy a is Here .

The answers are on Page 51
The use of flash cards may be helpful with these exercises.

1

a toy

2

a tree

3

toys

4

a toy in a tree

44

Write out correctly—

1 Here here and is is Peter Jane.

2 dog the Here is.

3 like like I I Peter Jane and.

4 Jane Peter a a and has has ball toy.

The answers are on Page 51
The use of flash cards may be helpful with these exercises.

1

2

3

4

Pages 46 to 51 give answers to the written exercises. They can also be used for revision and testing, before proceeding to Book 2a.

Page 4

Here is Peter.
I like Peter.

Page 6

Here is Jane.
I like Jane.

Page 8

Here is a dog.
I like the dog.

Page 10

Here is a shop.
I like the shop.

Answers

Page 12
Here is a ball.
I like the ball.

Page 14
Here is a tree.
I like the tree.

Page 16
Here is a toy.
I like the toy.

Page 18
The shop is here.
The tree is here.

Page 20

The dog is here.
The ball is here.

Page 22

1 Peter and Jane like the dog.
2 The dog likes the ball.

Page 24

Is Peter here? Yes.
Is Jane here? Yes.
Is the dog here? No.

Page 26

Is Peter in the shop? No.
Is Jane in the shop? Yes.
Is the dog in the shop? No.

Page 28

Has Jane a toy? Yes.

Has Peter a toy? Yes.

Has the dog a ball? No.

Page 30

Peter writes.

Peter likes to write.

I like to write.

Page 32

Jane writes.

Jane likes to write.

I like to write.

Answers

Page 34

1 Peter is in the shop.
  The dog is in the shop.
2 The ball is in the tree.
  Jane is in the tree.

Page 36

1 I like trees.
2 I like toys.
3 I like Peter and Jane.
4 I like dogs.

Page 38

1 Jane has the dog.
2 Peter has a ball.
3 The dog has a ball.
4 The shop has toys.

Answers

Page 40

1 Jane is here.

2 Peter is here.

3 I like the dog.

4 Peter and Jane like the dog.

Page 42

1 Here is a toy.

2 Here is a tree.

3 I like toys.

4 Here is a toy in a tree.

Page 44

1 Here is Peter and here is Jane.

2 Here is the dog.

3 I like Peter and I like Jane.

4 Peter has a ball and Jane has a toy.

New words used in this book

Total number of new words: 20
This book provides the link with writing for the words in Readers 1a and 1b.